THIS

SPOOKTACULAR

ANNUAL BELONGS TO

Phoebe Muirhead

age 6

to
Beautiful!

MONSTER HIGH

Distributed by D. C. Thomson Books Ltd.,
Courier Buildings
2 Albert Square
Dundee
DD1 9QJ

www.monsterhigh.com

ISBN 978-1-4723-6843-0

Printed in China

CONTENTS

A MONSTROUS WELCOME

Welcome to Monster High! Come in and pull up a chair. May I start by congratulating you on your choice of school – as you can see, we are quite literally head and shoulders above all the other institutions. Not only does our faculty contain some of the world's most monstrous minds, but our facilities, from our state-of-the-art grimnasium to our new vampitheatre, are also second to none. No wonder our OfDead rating is so spooktacular!

I am putting you in the capable (and removable) hands of one of our newest and most fiendly student bodies, Miss Frankie Stein. Frankie will give you a guided tour of the school. You'll get your scary bearings in no time! Over to you Miss Stein....

Are you ready to get scribbling? The best way to get your picture eek-xactly right is to copy each square into the blank one on this page. When you've finished drawing, colour the picture in.

CREEPATERIA
CLEO'S RA-CIPES

Eeeugh! Never in my 5,843 years have I tasted anything as disgusting as the slimy slop served up in the creepateria! I'm campaigning to have the menu changed to suit my – I mean, everybody's – tastes. These Ra-cipes have been passed down through my family over the millennia.

Try cooking à la Cleo for an authentic taste of ancient Egypt!

Creeperific Cucumber Dip

This is ugh-mazing served with toasted pitta bread! – Frankie Stein

You will need:

1 small cucumber
Pinch of salt
Handful of mint leaves
1 clove garlic, finely chopped (optional)
500g pot of plain Greek-style yoghurt
Drizzle of olive oil

You will not be using the sharp knives or the oven without asking for the help of a parent creature!

Here's what you do:

1. Slice the cucumber lengthways and carefully remove the seeds with a teaspoon.

2. Finely dice the cucumber into tiny chunks.

3. Place the cucumber into a shallow bowl and sprinkle with a pinch of salt. Leave for an hour until all the liquid has been drawn out of the cucumber.

4. While the liquid is draining from the cucumber, finely chop the mint leaves and the garlic. (Some monsters, especially vampires, don't like garlic, so you can leave it out.)

5. Drain the liquid away from the cucumber and combine the cucumber in a clean bowl with the yoghurt, garlic, mint and a drizzle of olive oil.

6. Chill the dip in the fridge before serving to your best ghoulfriends!

Deadly Delicious Dessert

This frozen feast based on Khoshaf sauce so yummy it would sweeten yeti!
– Abbey Bominable

For at least four servings, you will need:

- 140ml orange juice
- 300ml water
- 60g sugar
- 150g chopped dried apricots
- 100g sultanas
- 100g raisins
- 500g tub vanilla ice cream

Here's what you do:

1. Bring the orange juice, water and sugar to a boil in a small saucepan, stirring the mixture frequently.

2. Add the dried fruits, then bring the mixture to a boil again.

3. Simmer the fruits for 10 minutes before carefully removing from the heat. Allow the pan to cool slightly.

4. Place one or two scoops of ice cream in four small serving bowls.

5. Drizzle the warm fruity sauce over the top of each bowl. Freaktacular!

Scary-cool Fruit Snack

Eat these naturally sweet dates straight from the fridge, or try this twist for a glam party snack.
– Nefera de Nile

You will need:

- 250g pack of Medjool dates
- 100g milk chocolate
- Dusting of icing sugar

Here's what you do:

1. Break the chocolate into squares and place the pieces in a heatproof bowl. Suspend the bowl over a pan of simmering water, but do not allow the base to touch the water.

2. Heat the chocolate, stirring regularly, until it's almost completely melted, then remove it from the heat.

3. Dip one end of each date in the melted chocolate, then place it on a plate. Keep going until every date has been dipped. Put the dates in the fridge.

4. When the chocolate has set, sprinkle the dates with icing sugar. Serve them to your GFFs and wait for the screams of delight!

The Monster High-clopedia

In the libury there are many ancient books, including the Monster High-clopedia, which details the many lessons the student bodies have learned as they pass through the school. Here are two such tales....

TOUGH AS SCALES

One day in metalwork class....

Killer job on the stand, Jinafire!

The fire-breathing daughter of the Chinese Dragon had welded a mount for the winning casketball.

This ball's irreplaceable!

Careful, Flame-brain!

But while the guys were arguing ...

... the ball bounced through a window and fell down a well!

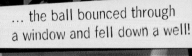

Step aside. Let Manny show ya how it's done!

We need to calculate the distance down and then ...

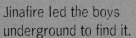

Jinafire led the boys underground to find it.

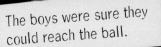

The boys were sure they could reach the ball.

The Monster High-clopedia

Here's another tale from The Monster High-clopedia. It shows the important lesson a new student taught us about never judging a book by its cover!

Ready, Wheeling and Able

The ghouls were discussing the new monster in school.

What's this new kid's name?

One morning, the school howlways rang with terrifying screeches....

Rider — bet he's a natural athlete!

Clawd would break a leash to get another guy for Skultimate Rollermaze!

Oh man! This place is spin-credible!

Suddenly something came flying round a corner....

From the look of his blog, this kid's pretty intense!

Oh hi! Monster High is totally a place where you can be yourself!

What're we gonna check out first?

Maybe we shouldn't show him ... all the sports stuff.

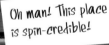

Penmanship class?

Awesome, right?!

What if he got hurt?

The worried ghouls took Rider somewhere safe....

We've got some voltageous activities planned.

Libury Club, Wool Collecting Club, Rock and Pebble Society....

This is what you guys do for fun?

Rider was horrified!

I heard so much spook-takular stuff about Monster High, but none of it's true!

Frankie ran Rider through the most boring clubs at Monster High.

I may have told him that Scream is the most epic thing you can possibly do!

Whooooo-hoooo!

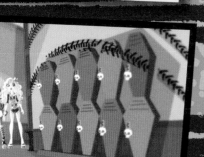

The ghouls looked everywhere for Rider.

Then Toralei slyly admitted she'd directed Rider towards the scream track.

Sure enough, Rider was burning rubber in the grim.

How could you let him on the scream track? It's not safe!

Maybe he knows better than us what he can and can't do!

Draculaura rounded on Clawd.

The werewolf told the ghouls that they were being over-protective.

Suddenly there was a crash!

The ghouls ran to check that Rider was OK....

This is who I am. If I need help, I'll ask. Cool?

Rider just wasn't a sit-around kinda dude!

I dunno.....

That was totally spin-sane!!! I'm going again!

Yeah.

Rider reminded Frankie that she'd said he could be himself at Monster High.

Will you light my wheels on fire? I wanna try this again!

THE END

THROW A DAY OF THE DEAD PARTY

Hola! I'm so excited that Headmistress Bloodgood is going to allow us to use the Great Howl for a Day of the Dead party this year. It is going to be so much fun! I cannot wait to introduce all the ghouls to my creeptastic culture.

The Day of the Dead is a holiday celebrated all across the world. On 1st and 2nd November, ghouls get together to remember fiends and family that have passed away. There are all kinds of parties and traditions. If you can't make it to Monster High this year, why not use Skelita's tips to skelebrate with your boos?

Even party ghouls need to be safe! Ask an adult before using scissors, skewers or sharp knives.

PAPER MARIGOLDS

YOU WILL NEED:

- Thin tissue paper in bright shades of yellow and orange
- Ruler
- Scissors
- Pipe cleaners or pieces of ribbon (one for each flower)

HERE'S WHAT YOU DO:

1. Layer five sheets of tissue paper on top of one another to make a pile. Trim them with scissors to create a 10 x 15 cm rectangle.

2. Starting at the shorter end at the bottom, fold up 2 cm of the stacked paper to begin making a fan.

3. Continue folding the paper until you reach the top.

4. Pinch the centre of the fan together, then tie it with a pipe cleaner or piece of ribbon.

5. Gently pull apart each layer of the fan until all the tissue forms the petals of a flower.

Sky Lit's Skeleton Cupcakes

YOU WILL NEED:

- 1 packet of cupcake mix
- White ready-mixed buttercream frosting
- Black icing pen
- Brightly coloured sweets
- Blue or pink icing pens (optional)
- Sugar sprinkles

HERE'S WHAT YOU DO:

1. Bake the cupcakes according to the packet instructions. Don't forget to ask your creator before using the oven.

2. When the cupcakes are cooked and cooled, scarefully ice each one with a thin covering of white buttercream frosting.

3. Draw a skeleton mouth on each cupcake using the black icing pen. Outline a thin smile with little black 'stitches' going across it like a railway track.

4. Now you can really get creative! Use sweets or icing pens to make the eyes, then top the outer edge of each cupcake with sugar sprinkles.

5. If you have room you could also use the icing pens to add extra flourishes to your cupcakes, such as swirly lines or flowers.

These cupcakes don't just taste good, they make a great party centrepiece!

CALAVERA SKULL MASKS

YOU WILL NEED:

- Pencil
- White card
- Scissors
- Colouring pens or pencils
- A skewer or sharp knife
- Piece of elastic

HERE'S WHAT YOU DO:

1. Draw a larger version of the Monster High Skullette onto a sheet of white card.

2. Cut out both of the eye holes.

3. Decorate the mask with beautiful flower designs in coloured pens or pencils. Use yellows, blues, greens, pinks and oranges.

These masks are a real Day of the Dead tradition in Mexico! If you don't want to make masks, you can use face-paints.

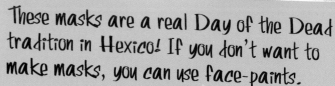
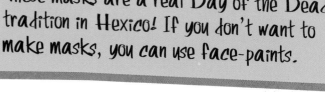

4. Scarefully make a small hole at ear level on each side of the Skullette with a skewer or sharp knife. Thread a piece of elastic through the back and tie it in place!

Fierce Green Fashion

Venus has got me thinking about how monsters have an impact on the environment. We've come up with some upcycling ideas to help ghouls look fierce whilst helping to protect the planet. We're displaying our creeptastic green collection in the school's Great Howl. Take a look!

Don't throw away your old clothes! Let Venus and Clawdeen inspire you instead. These scarylicious upcycling projects can all be made from a few old T-shirts.

You will need:

- Scissors
- Card
- Some old T-shirts
- Large beads
- Photo frame

Scary-cute Crop Top

Here's what you do:

1. Cut the sleeves and neck off the T-shirt.

2. Cut the T-shirt into a cropped top, leaving two long strips of material at the front.

3. Tug on the edges to make them look less freshly cut, then pull on the two strips so that they become more string-like.

4. Knot the two stringy strips together to create a cute tied detail.

5. Wear your crop top over a longer vest in a contrasting colour. Totally voltage!

Freaky-Funky Fringe Tank

Check with an adult before using scissors. Make sure it's OK before snipping a chunk out of any of your old clothes!

Here's what you do:

1. Cut the sleeves and neck off the T-shirt.

2. Starting at the front of the tee, cut vertically upwards from the hem to about a third of the way up. Repeat across the front so that the bottom hangs in a fringe of strings.

3. Pull on the strings to thin them out, then repeat the cuts along the back of the T-shirt.

4. Take a string and thread a coloured bead on to it. Tie a knot at the end to hold the bead in place.

5. Work your way all around the T-shirt, beading and knotting each string. You'll end up with a freaktacular beaded fringe that swishes as you move.

Nostalgic Tee Picture

Here's what you do:

1. Do you have a favourite T-shirt that's too small to wear any more? If you still love the picture on the front, cut it out!

2. Wrap the cut-out fabric round a piece of card, with the picture on the front. Then use tape or glue to secure the fabric at the back.

3. Fit the card into a photo frame to turn your old T-shirt into a piece of ugh-mazing art!

Bell Tower Beauties

Rochelle and I can both be found floating around the bell tower. I monster-watch from up here, looking for inspiration for my column. Rochelle just feels most at home when she's near (or on) the roof.

How well do you know Monster High's bell-tower beauties? Underline the words that sum up Rochelle in grey and those that make you think of Spectra in purple.

Rock Candy   Violet   Protective

Griffin   Silk   Angel Cake   Pale

Rhuen   Persistent   Transparent

Floating   Disgruntled   Chains

Roux   Scaris   Kind   Haunting

Defensive   Ferret   Curious

Iron   Stained Glass   Journalism

Architecture   Pigeons   Sculpting

Rattle   Ghostly Gossip   Grey

Answers on page 69

I gotta add this to my blog!

Boo la la! I cannot believe my eyes!

Spectra and Rochelle have a ghoul's-eye view of comings and groanings at Monster High. What do you think they've just spotted? Draw the scene here!

Meet the Staff

Portraits of the staff members are on the noticeboard outside the faculty lounge. Urgh-nnoyingly, Heath Burns has switched all the names around and removed the subjects they teach – he's soooo in dead-tention (again). Can you fix the board?

Draw a line through the teachers' names, then write the correct ones next to the pictures. When you've finished, add each teacher's subject, too. The list at the foot of the page will help you.

COACH IGOR
....
....
....

MR WHERE
....
....
....

MR MUMMY
....
....

1

2

3

HEADLESS HEADMISTRESS BLOODGOOD
....
....
....

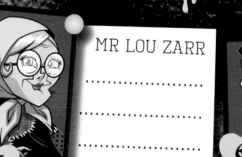

MR LOU ZARR
....
....

MR HACKINGTON
....
....

4

5

6

MR ROTTER
....
....
....

7

MR D'EATH
....
....
....

MS KINDERGRÜBBER
....
....
....

8

9

Headmistress   *Student Bodies Guidance Counsellor*   *Home Ick*
Dead Languages   *Maths*   *Mad Science*   *Drama and Li-terror-ture*

Answers on page 69   *Physical Deaducation*   *Trigular Calcometry*

Creature Teacher Quiz

Now that you have had time to look around the school, let's see how well you know my monstrously academic staff members. The answers are on page 69, but cheating will result in a spell in the Pit of Horror....

Take a pen and see how long it takes you to ace this quiz. Can you score ten right answers in less than ten minutes?

1. Complete Mr Mummy's favourite quote:

"Knowledge is the _ _ _ _
for every curse."

2. Mr D'eath has a habit of constantly sighing and keeps a 'regret list' about the things he wishes he hadn't done. True or false?

....

3. Which teacher has a qualification in Candy Construction?

....

4. "To see or not to be seen – that is the question," is the favourite quote of which teacher?

....

5. What is Mr Hackington more commonly known as among the student bodies?

....

6. Which faculty does Mr Mummy head up?

....

7. S.A.T.s are the regular examinations set by the staff of Monster High. What do the letters stand for?

....

8. Which unfortunately named creature is actually a supply creature, rather than a permanent member of staff?
A. Mr Mummy ☐
B. Mr D'eath ☐
C. Mr Lou Zarr ☐

9. In Home Ick, what skill does Ms Kindergrübber teach aside from cooking?

....

10. Which teacher once entrusted his students with looking after a gargoyle egg?

....

59

BEACHY KEEN

Gloom Beach is one of my favourite places in the world. Spending all day swimming in the ocean and all night in a dorm with my beast ghoulfriends – bliss! I was stoked to get hold of this great photo of us at Gloom Beach. I've made copies for all my GFFs!

Answer on page 69

One of Lagoona's prints is not quite the same as the other three. Can you spot the odd photo out?

Gloom-y Ghouls

It's another horrifically hot day at Gloom Beach and after playing water polo with Gil all afternoon, I just want to relax on a lounger with me mates. Trouble is, the vampires from Smogsnorts Academy have taken most of the loungers!

Which ghouls will be able to sit down and which ones will be left on the sand? Follow the trails of sun scream to find out.

Answers on page 69

Ghostcard From SCARIS

Oh, I am sooo 'appy! I 'ave receive a ghostcard from 'ome. I adore being at Monster 'igh, but sometime I cannot 'elp missing ze city and ze buildings where I grew up. If only I could read it!

Rochelle's ghostcard has been written on a stone tablet, but it's been monster-handled in the mail! Some of the vowels have chipped off. Can you fill in the gaps so that Rochelle can hear the news from Scaris?

BY AIR MAIL
PAR AVION

D__ar R__ch__ll__,

Gr____tings fr__m Scar__s!

__ll the G__rgoyl__s send th____r l__ve.
We m__ss s____ng y____r st__ny gaz__ ____cross
th__ r__oft__ps.

L__st week was f__shi__n week __nd Moanat__lla
Gh__stier st__ged her sh__w in the crypts __f
Ogre Dame Cath__dral. It w__s pr__tty
p____ktacul__r b__t n__t as ugh-m__zing as
Garrott du Roqu__'s. Your fr__end is r__ally
making a spl__sh w__th his l__test c__llection!

H__pe all's fr__aky-f__bul__us with you.

L__ve M__m & D__d xx

Answers on page 69

THE MAUL

What's in Store?

I just love the maul. Shopping is my favourite activity – being fur-rociously stylish, I love to spend my time checking out the fierce fashions in-store. I know every outlet like the back of my paw. What about you?

Do you know Clawdeen's favourite haunts? Unscramble the letters to reveal the most fabulous stores in the maul. The correct names are jumbled at the bottom of the page to give you a clue.

A HET FFICNO ABEN

_ _ _ _ _ _ _ _ _ _ _ _ _

F RANSLVANTYIA'S TECSCRE

_ _ _ _ _ _ _ _ _ _ _ _ , _ _ _ _ _ _

B RREBUFRY

_ _ _ _ _ _ _ _

E STRIEHOG

_ _ _ _ _ _ _ _

G KRAB BACOMS

_ _ _ _ _ _ _ _ _ _

C ACELOUGH

_ _ _ _ _ _ _ _

D HET DOOF TWALC

_ _ _ _ _ _ _ _ _ _ _ _

H IED-ERN

_ _ _ _ _ _ _

TRANSYLVANIA'S SECRET   DIE-NER   BARK MACOBS   FURBERRY
THE COFFIN BEAN
THE FOOD CLAWT   GHOULACE
GHOSTIER

64

Answers on page 69

They always have amazing films playing on the big scream in the maul's cinema. It's positively electrifying! It's where I took Frankie for our first — and last — date. I love watching horro-mantic comedies, but most of the monsters prefer to freak out at scary human movies.

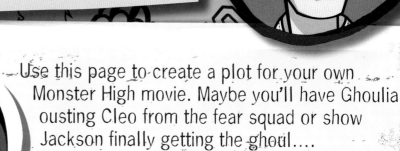

Use this page to create a plot for your own Monster High movie. Maybe you'll have Ghoulia ousting Cleo from the fear squad or show Jackson finally getting the ghoul....

COLOUR US CREEPY

I'm ghosting a creepover tonight, but before we get some sleep in my superking-sized coffin, I'm giving my GFFs makeovers in my powder room. Want to help? Make each ghoul look gore-geous!

Use your pens and pencils to give each ghoul a fangtastic new look.

Screams of Squares

You will need:

- 2 players
- A pen or pencil per player

Cleo is insisting that we play her favourite creepover game, Gargoyles to Gargoyles, but I'm putting my paw down. We always play that and she goes totally cryptic every time she loses! I'm suggesting my fabulous squares game instead. Want to play?

Rules:

- The aim of the game is to 'own' as many squares as possible. The squares that you own will be those with your initial in them.

- The youngest player goes first, joining two dots with a line. Play then passes to the next player, who draws another line. Each new line must connect with a line that's already on the board.

- Players continue to take turns until someone draws a line that completes a square shape. Any player completing a square should write their initial in the centre and take another turn. (You can just write over the Skullette if there's one in the square). The game continues until all the squares are complete.

- The winner is the player with the most points! Score 1 point for every square containing your initial. Score 3 points for every square containing your initial and a Skullette.

LATER, GHOULFRIEND!

ANSWERS

PAGES 22-23:
MY SPOOKY SCARE-ITAGE

Name: Skelita Calaveras
Dead-scended from: Los Eskeletos
Scary-cool country: Hexico
My scare-itage: I am very proud of my scare-itage and its legends and traditions. My favourite custom is *Dia de los Muertos* or Day of the Dead, where we honour our ancestors. We spend time with *la familia*, hold parties and decorate our homes with marigold flowers and screamily scrummy sugar skulls.

Name: Jinafire Long
Dead-scended from: Chinese Dragons
Scary-cool country: China
My scare-itage: The country of my fore-monsters is very eek-xotic with customs and traditions that have carried on for thousands and thousands of years. Monsters like me were often found guarding temples. We have always had great powers and can control elements including fire, wind and water.

Name: Cleo de Nile
Dead-scended from: The Mummy
Scary-cool country: Egypt
My scare-itage: My father tells me that traditionally monsters like me were entombed in pyramids in the middle of the desert with jewels and gold and sooo much bling. We still live in my father's pyramid and I have my own, totes amazing crypt! Our bodies were wrapped in an OTT amount of bandages – the updated version of this look we now call 'body-con'.

Name: Rochelle Goyle
Dead-scended from: The Gargoyles
Scary-cool city: Scaris
My scare-itage: Stone is a big part of my culture. My ancestors have always been found on and around great buildings such as castles and cathedrals, which we protect. Although I come from Scaris, monsters like me are found in many countries including ancient Egypt and Greece. We can take many forms.

PAGE 25:
LI-TERROR-TURE

1. HOLT HYDE
2. FRANKIE STEIN
3. VENUS MCFLYTRAP
4. CLAWD WOLF

PAGES 28-29:
GPA QUIZ

1. B
2. Casketball
3. HOME ICK
4. All of them – Frankie's currents cause problems in the water, Rochelle sinks like a stone and there is a large octo-creature lurking in the caves beneath the pool!
5. Mr Hackington
6. Mr Rotter
7. The catacombs
8. In their coffin lockers
9. True (although Lagoona sometimes smuggles in Neptuna, her pet piranha, in her water-filled bag)
10. Nightmare
11. C
12. A
13. They are all extra-scare-icular activities at Monster High

PAGE 32:
COUNSELLING CONUNDRUM

1. B
2. C
3. D
4. A

PAGE 33:
ZOMBIE SUPER-HIGHWAY

PAGE 34:
HEADS WILL ROLL!

1–D, 2–C, 3–E, 4–A, 5–B

PAGE 35:
BOO'S HOO IN THE 'COMBS?

1. Abbey Bominable
2. Jinafire Long
3. Toralei Stripe
4. Clawd Wolf
5. Skelita Calaveras
6. Venus McFlytrap
7. HooDude Voodoo
8. Draculaura

PAGE 41:
LAGOONA'S WATERY WORDSEARCH

The extra word is CHLORINE.

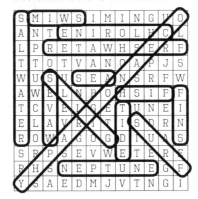

PAGES 56-57:
BELL-TOWER BEAUTIES

Spectra's words:
Violet, Angel Cake, Curious, Persistent, Floating, Transparent, Ghostly Gossip, Journalism, Haunting, Chains, Pale, Kind, Rhuen, Rattle, Silk, Defensive, Ferret.

Rochelle's words:
Rock Candy, Iron, Stained Glass, Griffin, Protective, Architecture, Grey, Sculpting, Roux, Scaris, Pigeons, Disgruntled.

PAGE 58:
MEET THE STAFF

1. Headless Headmistress Bloodgood
HEADMISTRESS

2. Mr Rotter
DEAD LANGUAGES

3. Mr Hackington
MAD SCIENCE

4. Mr Where
DRAMA AND LI-TERROR-TURE

5. Ms Kindergrübber
HOME ICK

6. Mr D'eath
STUDENT BODIES
GUIDANCE COUNSELLOR

7. Coach Igor
PHYSICAL DEADUCATION

8. Mr Lou Zarr
TRIGULAR CALCOMETRY

9. Mr Mummy
MATHS

PAGE 59:
CREATURE TEACHER QUIZ

1. "Knowledge is the cure for every curse."
2. True
3. Ms Kindergrübber
4. Mr Where
5. Mr Hack
6. Maths
7. Scary Aptitude Tests
8. Mr Lou Zarr ('Mr Loser', get it?!)
9. Sewing
10. Mr Hackington

PAGE 60:
BEACHY KEEN

B.

PAGE 61:
GLOOM-Y GHOULS

Only Ghoulia and Draculaura will get to sit on the loungers.

PAGE 62:
GHOSTCARD FROM SCARIS

Dear Rochelle,
Greetings from Scaris! All the Gargoyles send their love. We miss seeing your stony gaze across the rooftops. Last week was Fashion Week and Moanatella Ghostier staged her show in the crypts of Ogre Dame Cathedral. It was pretty spooktacular but not as ugh-mazing as Garrott du Roque's. Your friend is really making a splash with this latest collection! Hope all's freaky-fabulous with you.
Love, Mum & Dad xxx

PAGE 64:
WHAT'S IN STORE?

A. THE COFFIN BEAN
B. FURBERRY
C. GHOULACE
D. THE FOOD CLAWT
E. GHOSTIER
F. TRANSYLVANIA'S SECRET
G. BARK MACOBS
H. DIE-NER